Why Do I Wear a Mask, You Ask?

Staying Healthy During a Pandemic

by
Benjamin Sievers
Maxwell Senn

Designed and illustrated by
Andyyura

Imaginal Discs Press
La Jolla, California

The proceeds from the sales of this book will be given to Little Mercies and other nonprofit organizations that work to better our world.

Edited by Ruth Matinko-Wald

For information and bulk orders,
email benjaminlouissievers@gmail.com.

Imaginal Discs Press
La Jolla, California

Library of Congress Control Number: 2020925771
ISBN 978-0-9964013-2-6
Printed in the United States of America

When my big brother comes home from college,
he brings with him a lot of new knowledge.

From how to do a handstand with one hand,
to how to play piano with the college band.

But I wondered why this time he came home so early,
and why his hair was long and curly.

When he turned around, to my surprise,
he wore a big white mask right under his eyes.

"Big Brother, why are you wearing that mask on your face?"
I say as I jump all over the place.

"We're in a global pandemic right now," he said.
"I'm wearing a mask so germs don't spread."

"That sounds scary!" I said in a fright.

Big Brother responded without hesitation,
"Don't be scared.
What we must do is be prepared."

"Cover our mouths when we cough, because germs can spread to others. By covering, we protect our father, mother, sisters, and brothers."

Overjoyed to see Big Brother, our dogs slobbered and jumped
and wiggled and squirmed. Yet all I could think was,
"So, what are germs?"

To that question Big Brother replied,
"They're tiny particles in the air that can make us sick.
To keep ours in and those of others out, a mask does the trick."

"Is there anything else I should know to keep germs away? I'm willing to do anything you say!"

With a little laugh, Big Brother went on: "Tell an adult if you start feeling sick, whether it's a painful tummy or your nose is runny."

"I can do that,
but what about the mask?" I asked.

"Okay! I think I understand now!" I exclaimed.

"Thank you! I love it!
You're such a good brother!"
I said with a hug.

Then he said with a grin, "Let's bring our masks and head to the park!" And our dog agreed with a rollicking bark.

Benjamin Sievers is a college student and the second youngest of five brothers. He teaches science online to middle school students, plays classical piano, and is a passionate advocate for ensuring that at-risk populations have access to medical care. He is studying to become a medical doctor with a focus on infectious diseases. Ben is the recipient of awards for singing in a choir and for his efforts to advance global health and racial justice.

Maxwell Senn is a middle school student and the youngest of the five brothers. He spends his free time playing the piano, making YouTube videos, playing with the family dogs, and tossing frisbees with his older brothers. Maxwell and Benjamin both help with their family's nonprofits: Little Mercies, which serves migrant and orphaned youth in Mexico and Thailand; and the Stand For Courage Foundation, which strives to prevent bullying.